KJOS
CONTEMPORARY
COMBO
SERIES

GUITAR

Sessions
Book 1

Comprehensive Method
for Individual or Group Study
by KEVIN DALEY

USE OF THE TAPE AND BOOK

Becoming a well-rounded guitarist requires a thorough understanding of the basics of music and the guitar itself. Following this book page-by-page will give you the tools necessary to perform the music you want to play. Use the special features in **Guitar Sessions** to develop your new-found skills:

▶ Study the THEORY, CHORD, STYLE, and NEW NOTE boxes and complete the WORKSHOPS to strengthen your basic musical knowledge;

▶ Build your technique and knowledge of the guitar with LEFT HAND and RIGHT HAND boxes;

▶ Work with a teacher or friend to develop your ability to play with others through duets and teacher accompaniments;

▶ Play along with the accompaniment tape on the selections that have a cassette logo (▭). The tape contains accompaniments for each MINI-JAM and the five SESSIONS. The selections are mixed twice — first, for you to hear how your guitar part should sound; second, for you to play along. Use the tape counter spaces beside the logo to log each selection for easy access.

▶ Perform the SESSIONS with keyboard, drum set, and bass players. Their parts appear in the SESSIONS books for their instrument. These other parts are also recorded on your accompaniment tape.

▶ Read the next six pages carefully to learn the fundamentals of playing the guitar and use them for future reference.

ISBN 0-8497-2902-5

PARTS OF THE GUITAR

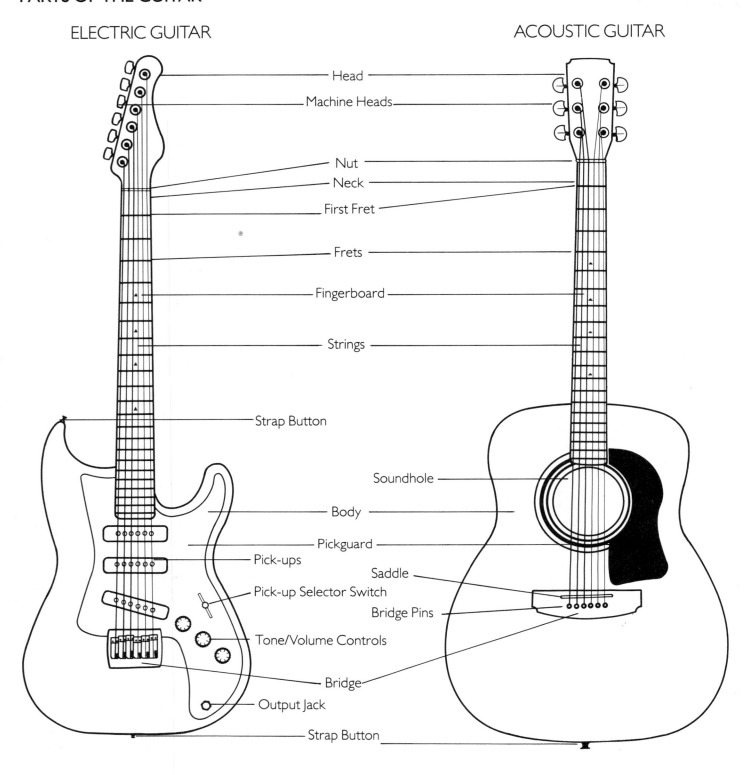

ELECTRIC GUITAR

ACOUSTIC GUITAR

Head

Machine Heads

Nut

Neck

First Fret

Frets

Fingerboard

Strings

Strap Button

Soundhole

Body

Pickguard

Pick-ups

Saddle

Pick-up Selector Switch

Bridge Pins

Tone/Volume Controls

Bridge

Output Jack

Strap Button

HOW GUITARS PRODUCE SOUND

All guitars produce sound in basically the same way. When you pick a guitar string, it vibrates and creates soundwaves which must be amplified. It is the way that a guitar amplifies or boosts the sound of the vibrating string that differentiates electric guitars from acoustic guitars.

On an acoustic guitar, the vibrations are transferred through the bridge and saddle and amplified acoustically — by the body of the instrument itself. On an electric guitar, pick-ups transform the energy created by the vibrating strings into an electrical signal, which travels through an audio cable to an amplifier. The amplifier magnifies and converts the signal into amplified soundwaves.

PLAYING POSITION

You may play the guitar while either standing or sitting.

SITTING

▶ Sit up straight on the front part of an armless chair. Relax your shoulders and upper body.

▶ Rest the guitar on your upper right thigh and tilt the guitar slightly back and against your body.

▶ Support and stabilize the guitar with the upper part of your right forearm, with your elbow bent at a right angle. Keep your right forearm and wrist in a straight line, angled slightly upward from the strings. Your left hand and arm should play no role in supporting the instrument.

▶ Position the neck parallel to the floor or angled slightly upward.

STANDING

When standing, the basic playing position is unchanged.

▶ Use a guitar strap to support the weight of the instrument. Always make sure it is securely fastened. You may wish to wear the strap even when seated.

▶ Adjust the strap to allow your arms and hands maximum comfort and mobility.

▶ Stand up straight with your shoulders relaxed and your feet slightly spread apart.

▶ Slightly increase the upward angle of the neck.

RIGHT HAND

RIGHT HAND TECHNIQUE

Your right hand is used to sound the strings, with either a guitar pick or your fingers. This book will concentrate solely on pick-style playing; finger-style playing will be discussed in later books.

THE PICK

Picks (or **plectrums**) vary in shape, size, gauge (or thickness), and material. Begin with a plastic or nylon pick of medium gauge and size, in the shape of a teardrop. As you become more familiar with the guitar, experiment with several types of picks to find your personal favorite.

HOLDING THE PICK

▶ Hold the pick firmly but not rigidly between your thumb and the side of your index finger. Grasp the pick near the center to expose only the point of the pick. The point should be at a right angle to your thumb.

▶ Loosely curl your other fingers in toward your palm.

PLAYING THE GUITAR

Use the pick to strike or pluck the strings. Your forearm, wrist, and finger muscles work together to create the **stroke**.

Acoustic Guitar: Strike the string over the soundhole.

Electric Guitar: Strike the string approximately halfway between the bridge and the fret closest to the bridge.

When the string is struck from above, with a downward motion, this is called a **downstroke**.

▶ When picking, your palm and fingers should not touch the strings. Remember to use only the point of the pick.

▶ Strive for an even, consistent tone and volume, using a minimum amount of arm and wrist motion.

LEFT HAND TECHNIQUE

Your left hand is used to change the length of the strings by pressing them against the frets. This allows the guitar to produce different pitches on the same string.

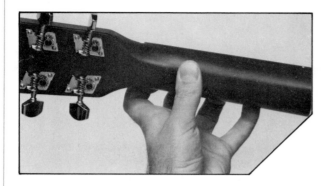

THUMB

▶ Place your thumb behind and at a right angle to the neck, pressing with the pad to properly counterbalance your fingers.

▶ Your thumb should not bend or curl over the top of the neck onto the fingerboard.

WRIST, HAND, AND ARM

▶ Bend your wrist to position your fingers over the fingerboard.

▶ Arch your fingers, keeping your palm and hand clear of the neck.

▶ Relax your shoulder, arm, and elbow and allow them to hang naturally.

FINGER AND FRET NUMBERS

Each fret is numbered; the fret closest to the nut is the first fret, the next fret toward the bridge is the second fret, and so on.

Each finger is numbered:
Index — "1" or first finger   Ring — "3" or third finger
Middle — "2" or second finger   Little — "4" or fourth finger

Each finger should always hover over its corresponding fret.

FRETTING STRINGS

When you press on a string, you are **fretting** the string. When the string is picked without being fretted, it is an **open string**.

▶ To fret a string, press firmly with your finger just behind the fret, not directly on the fret itself. For example, to play a note on the second fret, press just behind the second fret (toward the nut).

▶ Fret strings with your fingertips. Your fingernails must be trimmed so that you can easily press the strings down onto the fingerboard.

▶ In order to sound and ring clearly, strings must be fretted and picked simultaneously. Precise coordination of your right hand and left hand is essential.

TUNING THE GUITAR

Each open string must be **tuned** to a particular note or pitch. A string is identified by both pitch name and string number.

There are several methods of tuning, each involving **reference pitches**, which can be obtained from a variety of sources.

▶ The pitch name of each string corresponds to a note on a **piano keyboard** (see diagram).
▶ Pitches for each string appear at the beginning and end of each side of the **accompaniment tape**.
▶ A **tuning fork** or **pitch pipe** can also provide reference pitches.

For those with prior musical knowledge, you may notice that guitar music is written an octave higher than it sounds.

To tune a guitar string, pick it while listening to the reference pitch. While the string is sounding, alter its pitch by turning the machine head slightly. Tightening a string makes the pitch higher, while loosening it makes the pitch lower. (Start with the string slightly loosened and tighten it up to the correct pitch.) The string is in tune when its pitch matches the reference pitch exactly.

RELATIVE TUNING

Since the guitar can produce a particular pitch on more than one string, relative tuning is another effective tuning method.

1. Tune the sixth string (low E string) to a reference pitch as described above.
2. Press behind the fifth fret on the sixth string with your second finger and pick the note. Pick the fifth string (A string) immediately while holding the note on the sixth string. Adjust the pitch of the fifth string to match the sixth string.
3. Tune the open fourth string to the tuned fifth string, fretted behind the fifth fret.
4. Tune the open third string to the tuned fourth string, fretted behind the fifth fret.
5. Tune the open second string to the tuned third string, fretted behind the **fourth** fret.
6. Tune the open first string to the tuned second string, fretted behind the fifth fret.

When using this method, adjust the machine heads with your right hand so that your left hand can remain in place. Always listen carefully to the pitch you are tuning to, and try to hum or sing that pitch as you tune.

For ease and accuracy, some guitarists prefer electronic tuning devices.

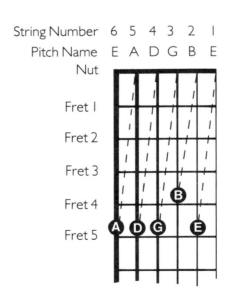

TIME

Playing music requires a good sense of **time** and the ability to feel a steady **beat** or pulse. To help develop this ability, many musicians practice with a **metronome**, a device which generates a steady pulse at various speeds, or **tempos**. While not absolutely necessary, working with a metronome is highly recommended.

EXERCISE A

The number of **beats per minute** that a metronome produces can be changed. Clap along with a metronome at both its lowest setting and its highest setting, as well as several in between. As you clap, repeatedly count aloud "1 - 2 - 3 - 4." If you do not have a metronome, clap along with a ticking clock or the recordings on your accompaniment tape.

EXERCISE B

Establish a slow steady pulse, counting aloud "1-2-3-4." On each beat, strike the first (high E) string by placing the pick above the string and striking it with a downward motion (a downstroke). Repeat this pattern several times.

PITCH

The highness or lowness of a musical sound is called its **pitch**. The first string is the highest-pitched of the open strings; the sixth string is the lowest-pitched.

EXERCISE C

Establish a slow steady pulse, counting aloud "1-2-3-4." On the first four beats, pick the first (high E) string, all downstrokes. On the next four beats, pick the second (B) string. Continue through strings three, four, five, and six (high strings to low strings), always maintaining the steady pulse. When you reach the sixth (low E) string, continue the exercise by reversing the order (low strings to high strings).

The pitch of a guitar string changes when the string is fretted. The higher the fret number, the higher the pitch.

EXERCISE D

Establish a slow steady pulse, counting aloud "1-2-3-4." On the first four beats, pick the open first (high E) string, all downstrokes. On the next four beats, fret the first string with your first finger just behind the first fret and pick four downstrokes, maintaining the even pulse. Repeat this exercise several times. The fingered note has a higher pitch than the open string note.

PITCH READING AND NOTATION

Music is written on a **staff**, consisting of five lines and four spaces.
Each line and space of a staff has a letter name. The first seven letters of the alphabet are used: A-B-C-D-E-F-G.
A **clef** appears at the beginning of every staff. Guitar music is written using the **treble clef**.

In the treble clef, the names of the spaces spell **FACE**.

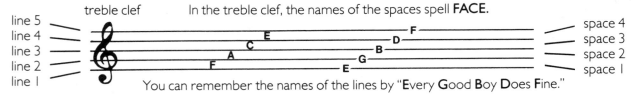

You can remember the names of the lines by "Every Good Boy Does Fine."

The treble clef is sometimes called the **G clef** because of the way it circles around the second line G.

Notes represent musical sounds. The pitch and letter name of a note are determined by where it falls on the staff.
Notes higher on the staff are higher in pitch. Notes lower on the staff are lower in pitch.

◄————————————— Lower   Higher —————————————►

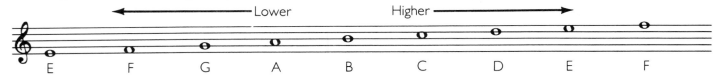

E   F   G   A   B   C   D   E   F

RHYTHM READING AND NOTATION

Rhythm refers to the duration and organization of notes in time.
The duration of a note is determined by the type of note used.

An open notehead is a **whole note**.   An open notehead with a stem is a **half note**.   A solid notehead with a stem is a **quarter note**.

Stems go up or down depending upon the placement of the note on the staff.
The duration of a whole note equals the duration of two half notes or four quarter notes.

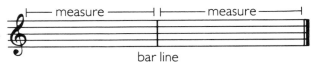

Bar lines divide music into **measures**.

A **double bar line** appears at the end of a piece of music.

A **time signature** appears at the beginning of a piece of music. In a time signature:

The upper number tells you the number of beats per measure.   There are four beats in each measure.
The lower number tells you the type of note that receives one beat.   A quarter note (as in ¼) receives one beat.

time signature (spoken "four-four")

These rhythm grids are used throughout this book. Each grid equals one measure in the given time signature.

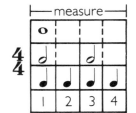

whole note receives four beats
half note receives two beats
quarter note receives one beat
beats per measure

Beats, or **counting**, may be written under notes as shown below.
Counting numbers connected by ties (‿) apply to the same note (the note lasts for the duration of those counts).

---

1. Draw the note indicated by the letter name.

A   D   G   E   B   F   C

2. Draw the bar lines and write the counting.

_____

NEW NOTES

A **fingerboard diagram** is used to show you how to finger new notes. It pictures a fingerboard with the head pointing upward (note the nut and the string thickness). A small "0" above a string or next to a notehead means open string.

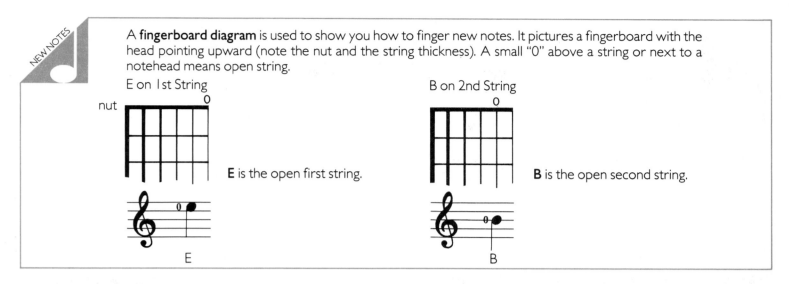

E on 1st String

nut

E is the open first string.

B on 2nd String

B is the open second string.

E

B

RIGHT HAND

downstroke (⊓) — pick with a downward motion

1. THE E STRING

▶ Pick all notes with a downstroke.

Count 1 2 3 4   1 2 3 4   1 2 3 4   1 2 3 4

2. THE B STRING

1 2 3 4   1 2 3 4   1 2 3 4   1 2 3 4

3. TWO STRING BLUES

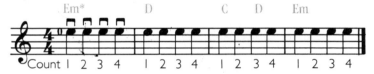

1   2   3   4   1   2   3   4   1   2   3   4   1   2   3   4

▶ Play these exercises at a comfortable tempo and with a steady pulse.

STYLE

In **Howlin'**, you will be playing a **melody** with the taped accompaniment. A melody is a succession of musical tones, the part of a song you usually hum or sing. (Make sure you have tuned to the pitches on the tape.)

4. HOWLIN' — Mini Jam

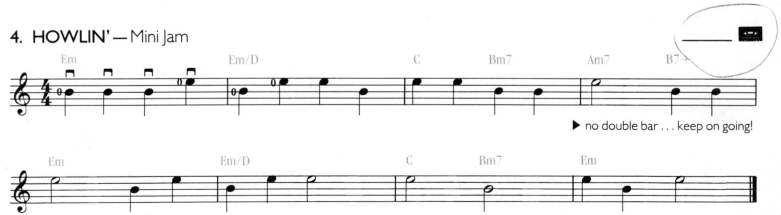

▶ no double bar . . . keep on going!

*These are **chord symbols**. When they appear in gray, your teacher or a friend may play them to accompany you.

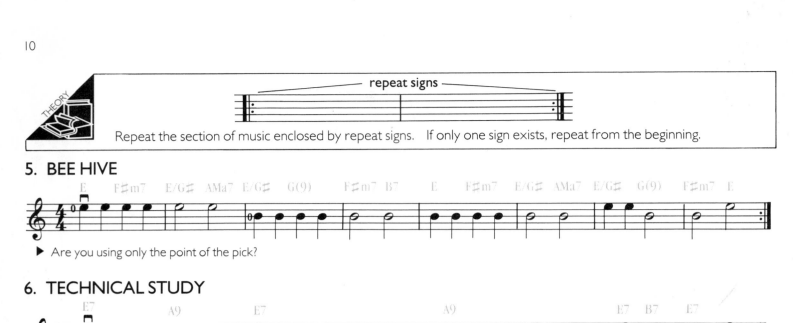

Repeat signs

Repeat the section of music enclosed by repeat signs. If only one sign exists, repeat from the beginning.

5. BEE HIVE

▶ Are you using only the point of the pick?

6. TECHNICAL STUDY

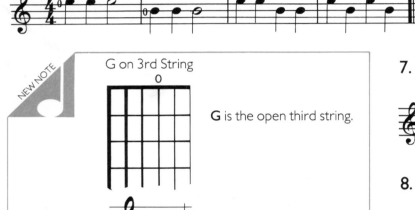

NEW NOTE

G on 3rd String

G is the open third string.

7. NEW GUY IN TOWN

8. DOUBLE TROUBLE

9. ALL THREE

1 2 3 4

▶ Count out loud while practicing.

10. POWER PLAY — Mini Jam

RIGHT HAND

Exercise 11 involves **string crossing**. Practice this exercise slowly and evenly to develop a feel for the distance between the E and G strings.

11. STRING CROSSING

12. OUT AFTER MIDNIGHT — Mini Jam

RIGHT HAND

doublestop — two notes played together

Doublestops are written as stacked noteheads and played by picking two adjacent strings with one stroke.

Exercise 13A: Play doublestops by placing your pick on the B string and picking a downstroke through both the B and E strings.

Exercise 13B: Since these doublestops do not involve the E string, follow the stroke through the G and B strings and stop the stroke with the E string. This technique, with the E string acting as a **barrier string**, is useful when playing this type of doublestop.

13A. DOUBLESTOPS

13B. MORE DOUBLESTOPS

14. GREAT BARRIER RIFF

THEORY

A **chord** is three or more notes played together.

Chords, like doublestops, are written as stacked noteheads, and are played with a single downstroke. All notes in a chord should sound as if they were struck at the same time. Chords often serve as the background for a melody.

15. TRIPLE DECKER

THEORY

fermata, or "hold" ⌒

Lengthen the duration of the note or chord by suspending the pulse.

16. HOLD IT

17. FERMATA STUDY

▶ Resume the original pulse after the hold.

18. DUET TO IT — Duet

▶ Practice both the **A** and **B** parts and play each with your teacher or with another guitarist.

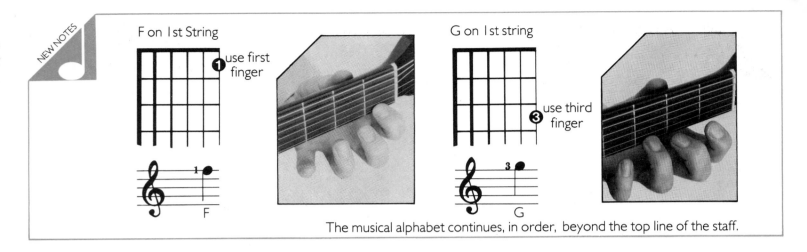

NEW NOTES

F on 1st String — use first finger

G on 1st string — use third finger

The musical alphabet continues, in order, beyond the top line of the staff.

LEFT HAND

When playing fretted notes like F and G, always use your first finger on the first fret, second finger on the second fret, third finger on the third fret, and fourth finger on the fourth fret. This is called the **finger/fret rule**. As a reminder, finger numbers will often appear alongside noteheads. Press just behind the fret, not directly on it. Fret and pick each note at the same time. Keep your left hand fingers in place on the fingerboard for the full duration of each note.

19. FIRST FINGER

20. THIRD FINGER

21. THREE'S A CROWD

22. BEYOND THE FIFTH LINE

23. EVENING SONNET

Student

Accompaniment

A **rest** is a period of silence. For every note value, there exists a corresponding rest value.

In $\frac{4}{4}$ time, a **quarter rest** ( ) receives one beat of silence.

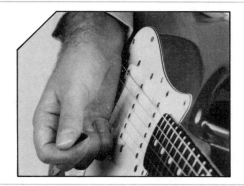

Since a rest indicates silence, you must stop the vibration of the strings whenever you see a rest. To do this, gently press the side of your right hand against the strings. This is called **string damping**. You should also damp at the end of every piece of music.

24. STRING DAMPING

25. AZTECA — Mini Jam

▶ You should be able to play **Azteca** without looking at your left hand!

TROUBLESHOOTING

Left Hand
- [ ] Pressing firmly behind fret
- [ ] Fingers arched
- [ ] Thumb straight
- [ ] Fingernails trimmed
- [ ] Palm not touching neck

Right Hand
- [ ] Pick held firmly
- [ ] Other fingers curled
- [ ] Using only point of pick
- [ ] Damping gently

Other
- [ ] Guitar in tune
- [ ] Fretting and picking notes simultaneously
- [ ] Guitar neck pointing slightly upward

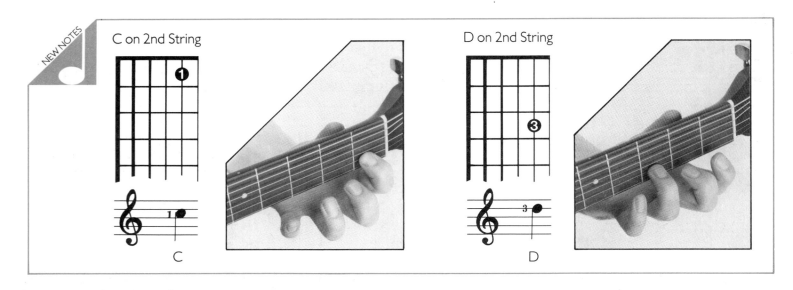

NEW NOTES

C on 2nd String

C

D on 2nd String

D

26. SECOND STRING STUDY

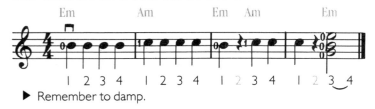

▶ Remember to damp.

27. ANOTHER NEW NOTE

LEFT HAND

Your fingers will have a tendency to flatten out when fretting notes. Make sure that your fingers are arched and not touching adjacent strings. Always press with your fingertips!

28. 2nd SECOND STRING STUDY

29. BACK AND FORTH

30. STORM CLOUDS

31. STAIRWAY

▶ Are you pressing firmly behind each fret and producing a clear, ringing tone?

32. ETUDE FOR NANCY

33. MARY ANN — Mini Jam

Traditional

34. SKIP TO MY LOU

Traditional

35. JINGLE JAM - Mini Jam

J. S. Pierpont

PRACTICE POINTERS

▶ Set a certain time aside every day for practicing. Short, regular practice sessions are more productive than longer, infrequent ones.

▶ Practice pieces slowly at first, and gradually work up speed. Using a metronome is helpful.

▶ Train your ear by watching your music carefully while listening to the demonstration mixes on your accompaniment tape.

▶ Have musical goals. When you have a specific set of goals in mind, practicing will be more enjoyable and beneficial.

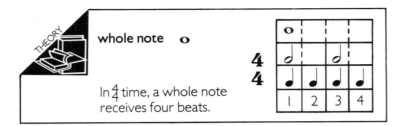

whole note o

In $\frac{4}{4}$ time, a whole note receives four beats.

36. WHOLE LOTTA COUNTING

37. LULLABY — Duet

One or more notes before the first full measure of a piece are called **pick-up notes**.

Count pick-up notes as if they were the last portion of a full measure.

38. PICK UP ON THIS

▶ Count "1-2-3-4-1-2" before beginning.

39. THREE TO GET READY — Duet

▶ Count "1-2-3-4-1-2-3" before beginning.

40. SAINTS — Mini Jam

Traditional

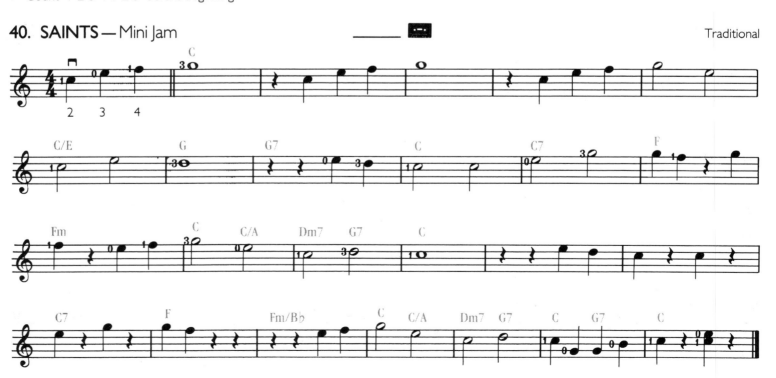

41. ONE MORE INNING

42. POWDER RIVER PASS — Mini Jam

NEW NOTE — A on 3rd String

43. THIRD STRING STUDY

44. TWO TONE ETUDE

45. LAMB JAM — Mini Jam
Traditional

46. AURA LEE
G. R. Poulton

47. THREE STRING CIRCUS

48. MINI SONATINA

49. ROCK EXPRESS - Mini Jam

50. MAY SONG — Duet

Sessions allow you to play with other musicians at your own level of advancement. Parts for a bassist, keyboardist, and drummer appear in **Bass**, **Keyboard**, and **Drum Sessions** Book I. Each Session is also found on your accompaniment tape, with both a demonstration mix and a performance mix provided.

SESSION

Your band (you and the other musicians) should set up so that everyone can see and hear each other easily. Don't set up all over the room or just for looks; a tight set-up is much better. The drummer and bassist should be especially close to each other. Likewise, the keyboardist and guitarist should be near one another. If you're using an amplifier, don't stand behind it. You've got to be able to hear yourself, too.

When playing with other musicians, always make sure everyone is in tune with one another. Also, work for good balance (relative volume) and a solid sense of time in the group. It's the way that musicians play **together** that makes a band sound great!

Catalina has a Spanish flavor, which requires a clean, crisp sound. Listen to the tape for an example. You play the melody throughout, so your part should be heard above the rest of the group. The keyboard plays chords, and the bass provides a solid single note foundation. The drums play a steady quarter note pattern.

Practice and perform the piece relatively slowly. The measures are numbered to make rehearsing easier. Boxed numbers are called **rehearsal numbers**, common places to begin when rehearsing.

Metronome setting ♩ = 104   Session 1 — **CATALINA**

A solid notehead with a stem and flag is an **eighth note**.

The duration of two eighth notes equals the duration of one quarter note. When a quarter note is equal to one beat (as in $\frac{4}{4}$ time), an eighth note is equal to one-half of a beat.

$$\quarternote = \eighthnote + \eighthnote$$

1 beat = ½ beat + ½ beat

When eighth notes appear in groups of two or more, they may be **beamed** together.

In $\frac{4}{4}$ time, the measure is divided into four beats. Eighth notes **subdivide** each beat into two parts. The subdivisions between the beats are called **offbeats** and are counted as "and" (written "&").

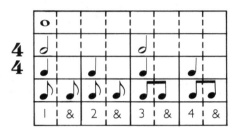

 Upstrokes are played by picking up from beneath the string. In music, these are noted with an upstroke sign (V). A combination of downstrokes and upstrokes is called **alternate picking**. Eighth note patterns should be played using alternate picking (upstrokes on the offbeats).

51. EIGHTH NOTES

▶ Keep a steady pulse — don't rush. Count the subdivisions.

52. ROAD RUNNER

53. THE TORTOISE AND THE HARE

▶ Use only the point of the pick!

54. SCOTLAND'S BURNING

Traditional

55. PINS AND NEEDLES — Mini Jam

56. TRICKY PICKING

▶ Leave your first finger down throughout measures 1 and 3; leave your third finger down throughout measures 2 and 4.

57. SIMPLE GIFTS

Shaker song

▶ Continue alternate picking.

1. Add eighth notes to balance the scales.

a. _____ b. _____ c. _____

An **interval** is the distance between notes with regard to pitch, measured in **half steps, whole steps,** or a combination. On the guitar, a half step is the distance from one fret to the next; it is also the distance from an open string to the first fret. Two half steps equal one whole step (whole step equals two frets).

In the musical alphabet, half steps occur between B and C, and between E and F.

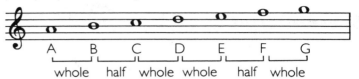

58. THE BULL FIGHT

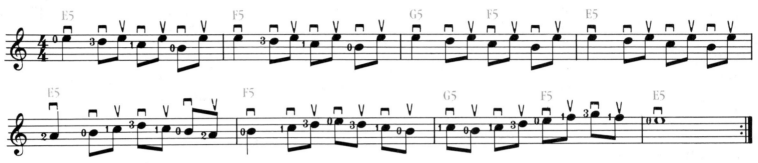

▶ Locate the half and whole steps in the second line of this piece.

59. GRAVEL HIGHWAY — Mini Jam

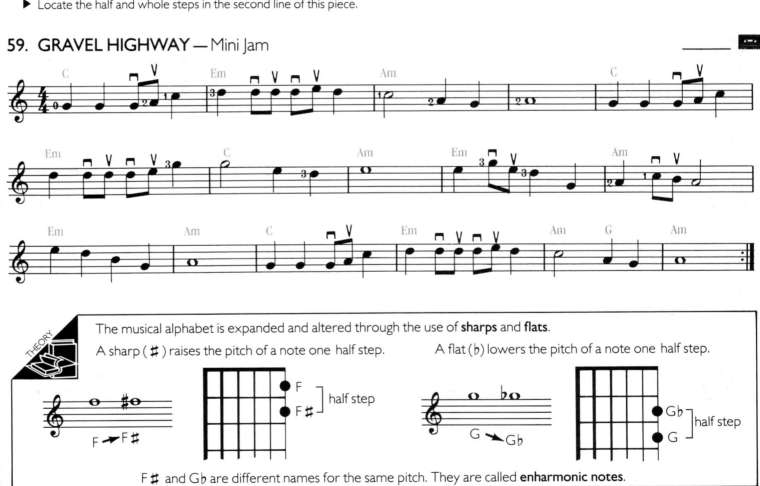

The musical alphabet is expanded and altered through the use of **sharps** and **flats**.

A sharp (♯) raises the pitch of a note one half step.

A flat (♭) lowers the pitch of a note one half step.

F ♯ and G♭ are different names for the same pitch. They are called **enharmonic notes**.

1. Indicate in the box the interval between each pair of notes.

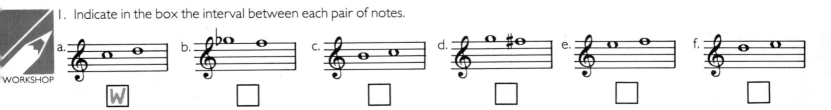

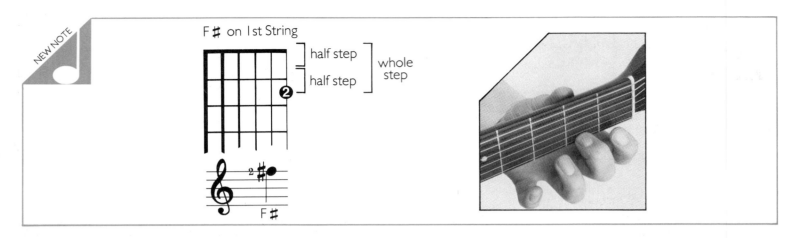

F♯ on 1st String

On the staff, a sharp or flat appears to the immediate left of the note it affects and remains in effect for all notes on the same line or space in that measure.

Always speak of a sharp or flat with the "sharp" or "flat" coming after the note name. For instance, F♯ is spoken "F-sharp," even though the sharp appears before the note in music notation.

60. LOOK SHARP

61. BLUE BELLS OF SCOTLAND

Jordan

62. GYPSY DANCE

In $\frac{4}{4}$ time, a **half rest** (—) receives 2 beats of silence.
Half rests normally sit on the third line of the staff.

In $\frac{4}{4}$ time, a **whole rest** (—) receives 4 beats of silence.
Whole rests normally hang from the fourth line of the staff.

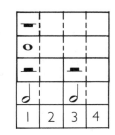

When you encounter rests longer than one beat, you need to damp your strings just long enough to stop the vibration. You do not need to leave your right hand on the strings for the full duration of the rest.

63. REST STUDY

64. RHYTHM RIFFS

▶ Practice these exercises slowly at first and then build up speed. Try using a metronome and/or counting out loud while you play.

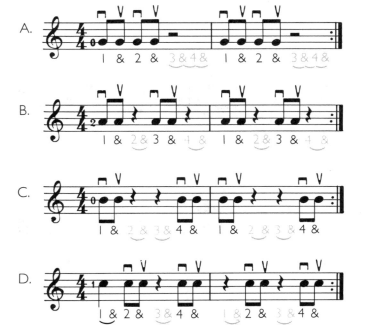

65. EIGHTH NOTE ETUDE

▶ When eighth notes are beamed together in groups of four, there is no change in the way that they are counted or played.

66. UPTOWN — Mini Jam

first and second endings

The first time through the piece, play the first ending and repeat as usual. The second time through, skip the first ending and play the second ending.

67. BLUES FOR ERIC — Mini Jam

68. EMBARCADERO — Mini Jam

Guitars are **polyphonic** instruments, which means that they are able to play more than one note at a time. Sometimes, two or more notes played together are written on the same stem. But when the notes that are played (or **attacked**) at the same time have different durations, they are written on different stems, one pointing up and the other pointing down.

In this dual-stem notation, you will often see notes and rests occurring on the same beat. These rests can not be damped with your right hand; instead, damp the note by releasing your left hand fingering when you reach the rest. Open string notes will ring until they fade naturally or until a note is fingered on that string.

69A. DOUBLESTOP PATTERN

69B. SEE THE DIFFERENCE

70. ODE TO JOY

Beethoven

The four (or more) musicians in a band must function together as a unit. While certain instruments may have more prominent roles from time to time, each instrument is equally important in developing the sound of the band. Even when performing as a **rhythm section** with a singer, horns, or a jazz ensemble, the guitar, bass, keyboard, and drums must think and play as a group within a group. Take responsibility for and practice your own part so you can concentrate on group playing in rehearsal.

Twin Town Tune is a rock and roll tune in the 1950's style. One of the characteristics of this style is the **backbeat** feel, or emphasis on beats 2 and 4. Listen to and feel the snare drum hits on these beats. You have the melody throughout the piece, so your part must be heard clearly. The keyboardist provides a solid eighth note chord background, and the bassist plays a single-note line that complements the melody. In measure 8, the drummer plays a **fill** to lead the group into the next measure.

Metronome setting ♩ = 100   Session 2 - **TWIN TOWN TUNE**

Every chord has a name, which is determined by the notes in the chord. The order of the notes on the staff does not affect the name of the chord.

In this book, a "chord window" shows the notes of a chord for easy reference. Be sure to memorize the notes and fingerings of every chord you learn.

An **E minor chord** consists of the three open strings E, B, and G. In chord notation, it is written **Em** (minor chords are written with a capital letter followed by a small "m").

A **C major chord** consists of open string E, 2nd string C, and open string G. In chord notation, it is written **C** (major chords are written with a capital letter alone).

E minor (Em) chord

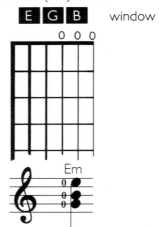

window

C major (C) chord

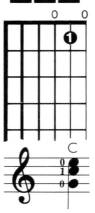

Playing chords in a rhythmic pattern is called **strumming**. In popular music, repeated strumming patterns help to establish a rhythmic feel or groove.

71. THE FIRST CHORD RETURNS

72. E MINOR STRUM

▶ Remember to damp on the rests.

73. C MAJOR STRUM

▶ Are you arching the fingers of your left hand and pressing with your fingertips?

74. DOUBLE PLAY

▶ You should be able to read both the chord symbols and the notes on the staff.

When the notes of a chord are played one after another and with separate pick strokes, this is called an **arpeggio**. Before playing an arpeggio, form the entire chord with your left hand.

75. BREAK IT UP

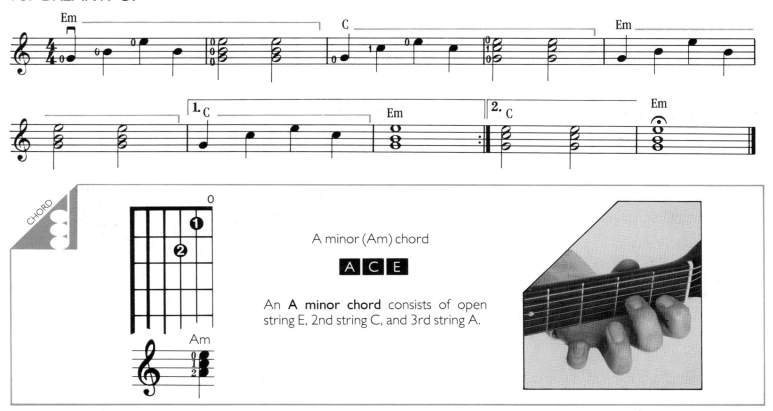

A minor (Am) chord

A C E

An **A minor chord** consists of open string E, 2nd string C, and 3rd string A.

76. A MINOR STRUM

▶ Are your fingers arched?

77. ARPEGGIO WORKOUT

In **Strum Time Soon**, you will be playing **harmony**. Harmony refers to the chords in a piece of music that provide the background for the melody (played on the tape in this case by another guitarist).

78. STRUM TIME SOON — Mini Jam

When strumming eighth note chord patterns, use alternate picking (downstrokes on the beats, upstrokes on the offbeats). However, striking all the notes of a chord on an upstroke can be awkward at faster tempos. Instead, many guitarists find it easier to omit the lowest-pitched string on chord upstrokes.

This: instead of this:

Though this is a popular technique, eighth note chord patterns are still notated completely.

79. STRUM PATTERN I

80. STRUM PATTERN II

81. SCOTT'S STRUM

Minor Thoughts is a duet mini jam, which means that you can play both parts with the taped accompaniment. When you play the A (melody) part, you are the **lead** guitarist. When you play the B (harmony) part, you are the **rhythm** guitarist. Both lead and rhythm styles serve an important musical function.

82. MINOR THOUGHTS — Duet Mini Jam

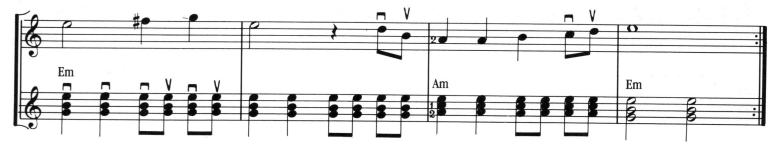

Guitar music is often written with only chord symbols and **slashes** with rhythmic values. Strum the chords following the indicated rhythm. Diamond-shaped noteheads designate half notes or whole notes. To read slash notation, you must have all chord fingerings memorized.

83A. RHYTHMIC STRUMS

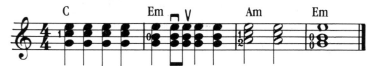

83B. SAME RHYTHMIC STRUMS

▶ This is exercise #83A using slash notation.

one-measure repeat sign   **⁒.**   Repeat the previous measure.

84A. TOM CAT

84B. COPY CAT

▶ This is exercise #84A using the one-measure repeat sign.

85. WE'RE HAVING STRUM FUN NOW

86. BULL'S-EYE - Mini Jam

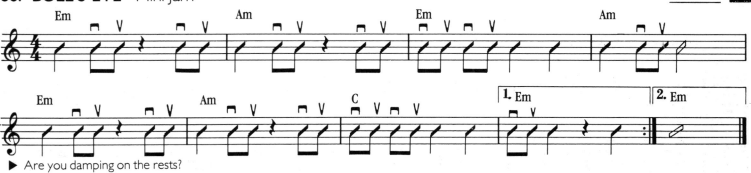

▶ Are you damping on the rests?

87. OPUS 87

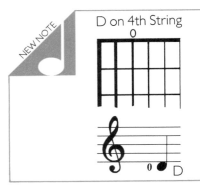

NEW NOTE — D on 4th String

D is the open fourth string.

The musical alphabet continues, in descending order, below the bottom line of the staff.

88. NEW STRING

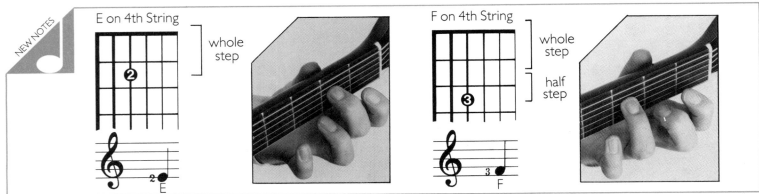

NEW NOTES — E on 4th String / F on 4th String

89. NEW NOTE

▶ Fingers arched? Playing with fingertips?

90. ANOTHER NEW NOTE

91. FOURTH STRING MARCH

92. TWO BASE HIT

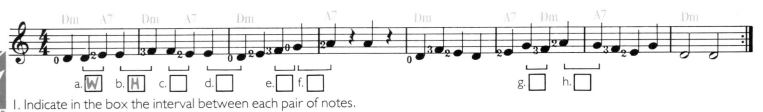

1. Indicate in the box the interval between each pair of notes.

WORKSHOP

93. VICTORY — Mini Jam

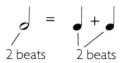

A **dot** (•) added to any note increases the duration of the note by one-half its original value.

For example, in 4/4 time, a half note receives two beats. The dot increases the note value by half (one beat). Therefore, a **dotted half note** receives three beats.

2 beats	2 beats
2 + 1 beats	2 + 1 beats

3/4 Time Signature

The upper number tells you the number of beats per measure. The lower number tells you the type of note that receives one beat.

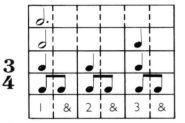

spoken "three-four"

There are three beats in each measure. A quarter note (as in 1/4) receives one beat.

Note and rest values are the same in 3/4 time as in 4/4 time. However:

▶ whole notes do not appear in 3/4 time.
▶ whole rests indicate a full measure of rest.

---

94. COUNT THREE

▶ Count the three beat pulse aloud.

95. TRICKY RHYTHM

96. WE THREE KINGS

J. H. Hopkins

97. UMI

Japanese folk song

98. MORSE CODE

99. MINOR MOVES

100. CIELITO LINDO — Mini Jam

Mexican folk song

101. BLOW THE MAN DOWN

Traditional

1. Use either a half note or a dotted half note to balance the scales.

a.

b.

c.

2. Draw the ties and circle the rests in the counting.

1 & 2 & 3 &   1 & 2 & 3 &   1 & 2 & 3 &   1 & 2 & 3 &   1 & 2 & 3 &

3. Draw the bar lines and write the counting.

102. THE MERRY WIDOW

Lehar

103. WALTZING TO WACO — Mini Jam

104. BAR BELL — Mini Jam

105. OUT WEST

THEORY — "common time" — time signature — means the same as $\frac{4}{4}$

▶ Practice with a slow, steady tempo; try using a metronome to work up speed.

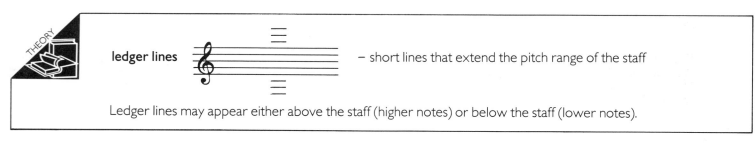

THEORY

ledger lines — short lines that extend the pitch range of the staff

Ledger lines may appear either above the staff (higher notes) or below the staff (lower notes).

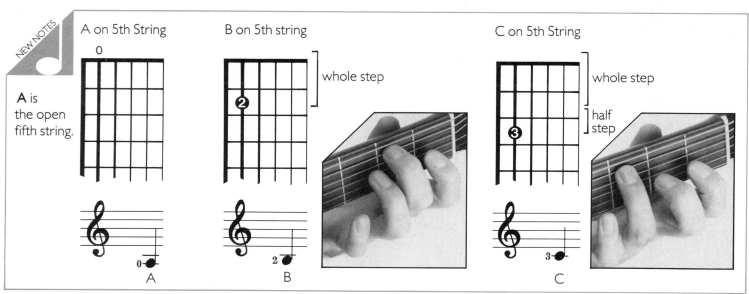

NEW NOTES

A is the open fifth string.

A on 5th String

B on 5th string

C on 5th String

106. OPEN STRINGS

107. NEW NOTE B

108. NEW NOTE C

109. FIFTH STRING STRUT

110. LONDON BRIDGE

Weatherly

111. RIFF FOR CHUCKEE

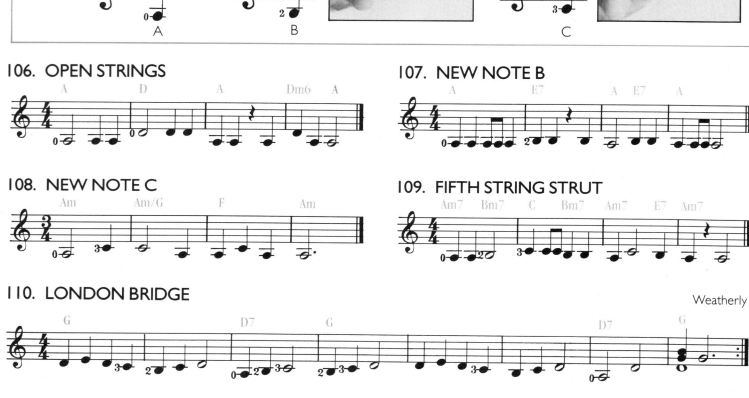

112. SEAGULLS

SESSION

Although each instrument in a band is equally important, one band member (it doesn't matter who) should be the leader. Leaders have many responsibilities, but two of the most important are counting off and cutting off the band. When counting off, you set the tempo and make sure everyone starts at the same time. The leader sets an imaginary metronome clicking in everyone's head. When cutting off, you make sure that everyone stops or **releases** at the same time. This is especially important when the song ends with a fermata. The band should work out verbal or visual cues from the leader for count-offs and cut-offs.

In **Don't Get Me Wrong**, you play both lead and rhythm at various points. When playing rhythm, don't play too loud and get in the way of the keyboard melody. When you have the melody at measure 9, come up in volume by picking a little harder. At measure 17, the keyboard takes over the melody again—work for good balance. Passing the melody around like this creates a more interesting arrangement.

Metronome setting ♩ = 96   Session 3 — **DON'T GET ME WRONG**

LEFT HAND

When playing certain chords, doublestops, and melodies, it is necessary to break the finger/fret rule. The first doublestop in **Metal Lake** is an example. Normally, your second finger would fret the A; however, that finger is already being used to fret the E. Therefore, you must break the finger/fret rule and play the A with your third finger. Make sure that both fingers are arched and close to the fret. Continue to follow the finger/fret rule wherever possible, and observe the fingering numbers when breakages must occur.

113. METAL LAKE

THEORY

Chord voicing refers to the order, doubling, and distribution of the notes in a chord.

On the left is the familiar voicing of the E minor chord. You can expand the chord by adding another E, below the G. The E is said to be **doubled**. Even though the voicing on the right has more notes and a different lowest note, it is still an E minor chord.

E doubled

Em   Em

On the left is the familiar voicing of the A minor chord. On the right, two notes (the A and E) are doubled. This voicing has more notes, but is still an A minor chord.

E doubled

A doubled

Am   Am

The letter name of a chord refers to its **root**. For example, the root of an A minor chord is A.
In a chord voicing, if the root of the chord is the lowest sounding note, the chord is in **root position**.
If any note other than the root is the lowest sounding note, the chord is in **inversion**.

Am   Am   Em   Em
(in root position)   (in root position)   (in inversion)   (in root position)

The chords you already know can be expanded to include notes on the fourth and fifth strings. Unless otherwise specified, play these new chord forms from now on.

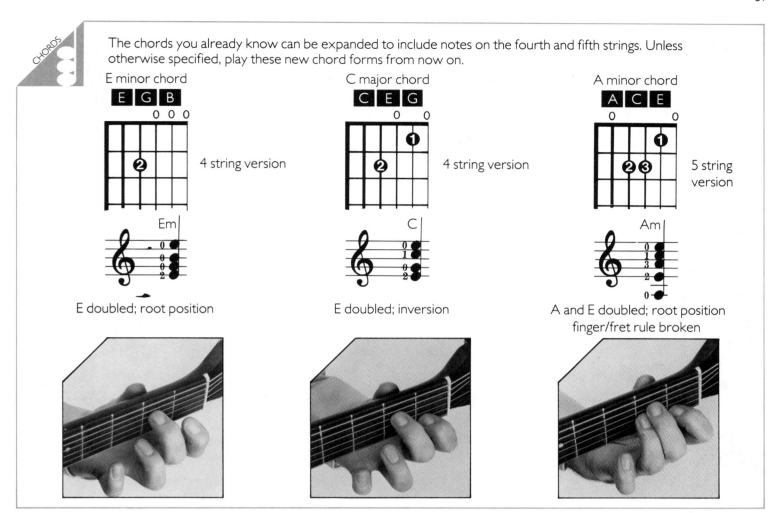

E minor chord
| E | G | B |

4 string version

Em
E doubled; root position

C major chord
| C | E | G |

4 string version

C
E doubled; inversion

A minor chord
| A | C | E |

5 string version

Am
A and E doubled; root position
finger/fret rule broken

114. STRUM WORKOUT I

115. STRUM WORKOUT II

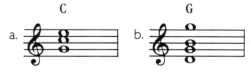

1. In a D minor chord, the notes are D, F, and A. The root of the chord is _____. The chord is in root position if _____ is the lowest sounding note. If _____ or _____ are the lowest sounding notes, the chord is in inversion.

2. Are the following chord voicings in root position or inversion?   a. 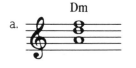   C   b.   G   c.   Dm

_____   _____   _____

3. Add (double) the note that will create a root position voicing of the chord.   a.   Dm   b.    Am

A **power chord** is a two-note chord voicing (one chord tone is omitted) usually played in a steady rhythmic pattern on the lower or **bass** strings. In chord notation, power chords are written with a letter name (the root) followed by "5" (see exercise #116). Playing power chords is a popular rock rhythm guitar technique.

Play all power chords with downstrokes. The solid, bottom-heavy sound comes from always striking the root first.

When playing power chords, the barrier string technique may be helpful.

116. POWER CHORD RIFF I

117. POWER CHORD RIFF II

118. DE-JAH-VOO — Duet Mini Jam

119. STONEBREAKER

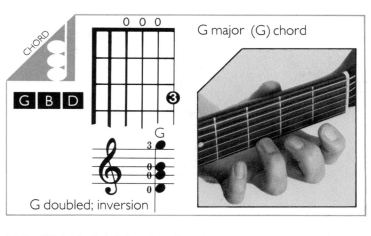

G major (G) chord

G doubled; inversion

120. NEW CHORD

121. MIX IT UP

122. TWO BARS PER CHORD

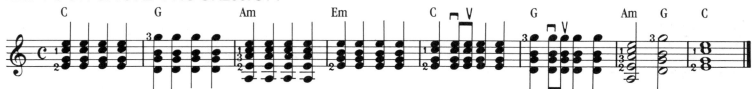

 A sequence of two or more chords is called a **chord progression**. (Note that the progressions of #123 and #124 are identical.) Chord progressions are also referred to as **changes** in jazz and pop music.

123. FOUR CHORD PROGRESSION

124. GONNA BE SOME CHANGES MADE

125. IRISH STEW — Duet Mini Jam

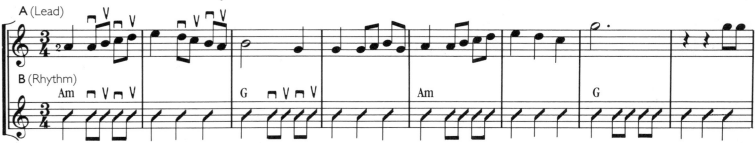

Pick-strum style is a popular technique in country and folk music. The bass strings are used to play a **bass line** on the **strong beats** of the measure (beats 1 and 3 in $\frac{4}{4}$ time; beat 1 in $\frac{3}{4}$ time). The strums are played on the higher strings on the remaining **weak beats**.

126A. FIRST BASS LINE

126B. FIRST BASS LINE WALTZ

127. SHORT SOLO

128. RHYTHM RIFFS

▶ These are common strumming patterns. Practice the chord changes slowly and evenly.

A.

C.

B.

D.

Often, rhythm guitar music is written in slash notation without specific rhythms. In this case, the slashes show only the basic pulse, leaving the guitarist to supply an appropriate rhythmic background following the chord progression. The background pattern is determined by the style of the music.

Cinnamon Toast uses this type of slash notation. Use the following strumming patterns when playing the progression.

| first time | second time | third time | fourth time |

129. CINNAMON TOAST — Mini Jam

(4 times)

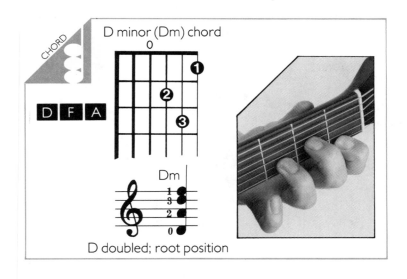

D minor (Dm) chord

D F A

Dm

D doubled; root position

130. D MINOR CHORD

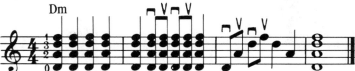

131. SHORT PROGRESSION

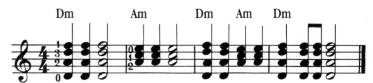

▶ By using the three-string version of the A minor chord, you can keep your second finger in place when changing to or from D minor.

132. RICHTER SCALE — Duet Mini Jam

▶ **Richter Scale** has two rhythm guitar parts; the lead guitar part is on the tape in all three mixes.

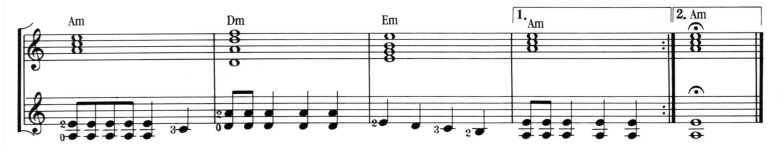

133. RHYTHM RIFFS

▶ Remember to damp on the rests.

134. REGGAE IN MIND — Duet Mini Jam

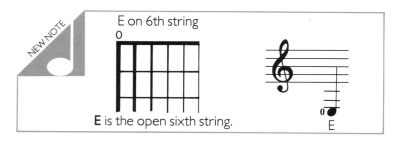

NEW NOTE

E on 6th string

E is the open sixth string.

135. BASS STRINGS

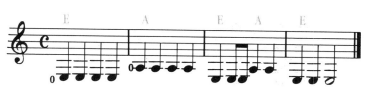

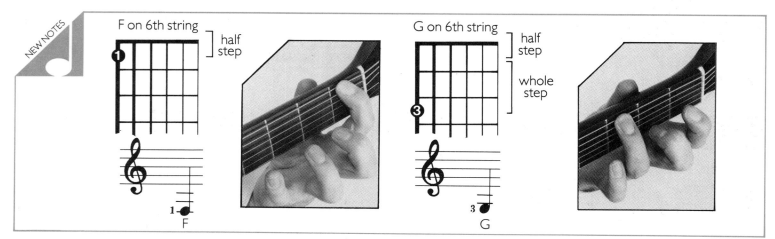

NEW NOTES

F on 6th string — half step

G on 6th string — half step, whole step

136. HALF STEPPIN'

▶ Note the similarities between the first and sixth strings.

137. HALF PLUS WHOLE

138. SIXTH STRING STRUT

139. SIX STRING REVIEW

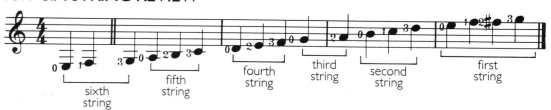

sixth string   fifth string   fourth string   third string   second string   first string

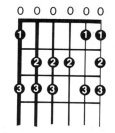

140. HARPSICHORD PLAYER

J. S. Bach

141. WISHFUL THINKING

142. ETUDE

Island Breeze is a rock ballad, and you play various rhythm guitar styles throughout. Make sure that the transitions are smooth (from arpeggiated chords at measure 1 to power chords at measure 9 to strummed chords at measure 17) and a steady groove is maintained. A solid sound and sense of time is especially important at slower ballad tempos. Try to lock in rhythmically with the bassist and drummer, hitting all the beats at the same time. Remember that you are providing the harmonic and rhythmic background, so play slightly "underneath" the keyboard melody. Underneath does not mean less intense, though. It takes as much concentration to play a slow, background rhythmic pattern as it does to play a fast, loud lead part.

Metronome setting ♩ = 88

Session 4 — **ISLAND BREEZE**

THEORY

natural ♮
- cancels a sharp or flat for the duration of a measure

143. IT'S ONLY NATURAL

144. RED SHOES — Mini Jam

THEORY

Sharps or flats immediately following the clef are called the **key signature**. The key signature identifies the **key** of the piece. The sharps or flats affect every note in the piece on that line or space, unless temporarily cancelled by a natural.

In the key of **G major**, there is one sharp (F♯) in the key signature.

Key of G major:  key signature

This means to raise every F in the piece to F♯ (one half step).

145. LULLABY

Brahms

THEORY

A **scale** is a succession of notes ascending or descending from a given note (called **tonic**) to a note one **octave** higher or lower (the next highest or lowest pitch with the same name). Every key signature has a corresponding **major scale** which has the same letter name and contains the same sharps or flats, using all the letters of the music alphabet once.

G major scale.

G A B C D E F♯ G F♯ E D C B A G
tonic   tonic   tonic
     octave   octave

Practice and memorize the G major scale in both ascending and descending order.

146. G MAJOR SCALE ETUDE

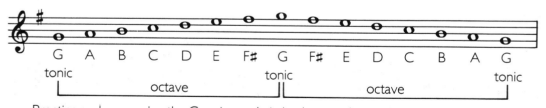

A major scale can begin on any note. Each major scale contains a specific pattern of half steps and whole steps.

G major scale

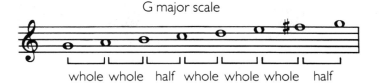

whole   whole   half   whole   whole   whole   half

Using this pattern, you can build a major scale starting on any note.

C major scale

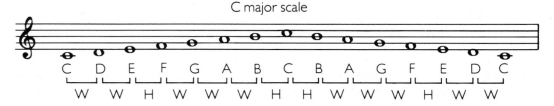

C D E F G A B C B A G F E D C

W W H W W W H H W W W H W W

The C major scale uses all the letters of the musical alphabet once, with no sharps or flats. Therefore, the C major key signature contains no sharps or flats.

Key of C major: ←— key signature

147. C MAJOR SCALE ETUDE

148. CAN-CAN

Offenbach

▶ The notes of the major scale are the foundation for many melodies. Notice how **Can-Can** uses the C major key signature and all the notes of the C major scale.

149. CAN-CAN

Offenbach

▶ This is the same melody as #148, but in the key of G major.

LEFT HAND

Practicing scales (and simple patterns based on them) during each practice session is a good way to develop left hand technique. Start slowly, and gradually build up speed. Memorize every new scale you learn.

150A. THIRDS IN C

150B. THIRDS IN G

THEORY

Chords are related to keys and scales. The **tonic chord** has the same name as the related scale and key and is constructed from the tonic, third, and fifth notes of the scale. These chord tones are known, respectively, as the **root**, **third**, and **fifth**. This three-note chord is sometimes referred to as the **tonic triad**.

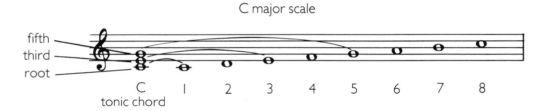

C major scale

fifth
third
root

C tonic chord 1 2 3 4 5 6 7 8

The tonic chord functions as "home base," often appearing at the beginning and end of a piece of music.

151. G TONIC WALTZ

1. Using the correct key signature, write a G major scale on the staff below. Write the pattern of half and whole steps beneath. Identify tonic.

2. Next to the scale, write the tonic triad in the key of G in both root position and in inversion. Circle the root in each.

WORKSHOP

152. HAPPY TO BE GOIN' HOME — Mini Jam

▶ The naturals in the first and second endings cancel (for those measures only) the # in the key signature.

It's possible to play a major scale entirely on one string now that you know:
▶ the scale pattern of whole and half steps;
▶ the distance between frets is a half step;
▶ the distance between two frets is a whole step.

With this information, try playing a major scale on the third, or G string. Use your first finger to play each note.

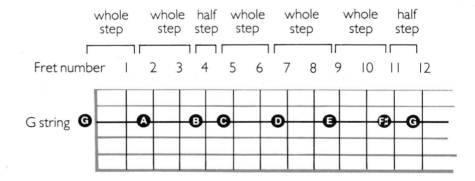

This scale should sound like the G major scale you played with your usual fingerings (called **first position** fingerings). As you can see, notes appear more than once on the fingerboard of the guitar.

You have the lead part throughout **Off The Hook**. Listen to the other parts and notice how your part plays off the others without competing with them. Each part has a particular function. The overall sound of the individual parts meshing together is what makes an arrangement of a song effective.

As a way to develop a steady sense of time in your band, try the following exercise with this piece and others. Play two measures; then rest for measures three and four without counting outloud; then try to come back in together at measure five. Continue this two bar pattern throughout the piece. Once you have this down, try it with four or eight measures of rest.

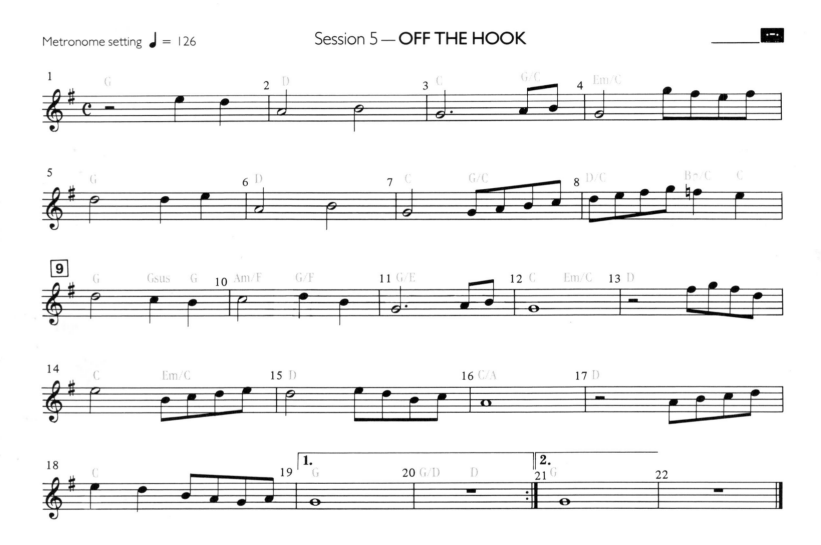

Dear Student,

Congratulations on completing **Guitar Sessions** Book 1! You're now well on your way to a rewarding hobby or a successful career with the guitar.

Building from the fundamental musical knowledge you now possess, **Guitar Sessions** Book 2 will take you beyond the basics to the more advanced world of musicianship. Not only will you learn more chords (including seventh chords and bar chords), but you'll learn how chords are constructed and how they function within a song. You'll learn the Blues and many other song forms, and you'll learn the rest of the notes in first position. All this, plus more solos, duets, mini jams, and sessions.

I hope you enjoyed Book 1 as much as I enjoyed writing it. Best of luck to you.

Kevin Daley